TAKING SHELTER

Alan Dapré

Illustrated by
Kim Palmer

Series Editors
Steve Barlow and Steve Skidmore

Taking Shelter

For Charlie, Jean and Ted, growing up during the Second World War, air raids have become almost a normal part of life. When the air raid siren sounds this time, they are alone in the house, waiting for their mum to come home from the munitions factory. They are so used to the routine of taking shelter from bombs and flak that they sometimes forget about the real danger of being caught in an air raid. But during this play they get a reminder of just how dangerous life in wartime can be.

The Characters

Charlie

Charlie is eleven. He is the oldest, and he has been left with the job of looking after his younger brother and sister while their mum is out. He is quiet and thoughtful, but he has to spend a lot of time chasing after Ted, trying to stop him from getting into trouble. Sometimes Charlie is really frightened during the bombing raids, but he does not want Ted and Jean to see this.

Ted

Ted is eight. He is interested in collecting all sorts of things, from comics to shrapnel. He is always getting into trouble, and sometimes he thinks Charlie is too bossy. Ted finds the war exciting, but he does miss his dad, who is away fighting, and he gets worried when his mum is out at the factory – not that he would ever tell Charlie or Jean this.

Jean

Jean is nine. She belongs to the Girl Guides, and does a lot of voluntary work to help the war effort. She gets quite nervous during the bombing raids, and worries that something might happen to her family. Charlie tries to make her less worried by cracking jokes or playing games in the shelter.

The scene:

July 1944. The action on stage takes place in the front room of a terraced house in the south-east of England.

The play begins with three children in view. Jean is centre stage, leaning against a large table, drawing faces on a sheet of newspaper.

Charlie sits on a chair, stage right, reading a book.

Ted paces slowly around the room, hands in his pockets. He walks to the rear of the stage then, in mime, draws back a heavy blackout curtain.

Ted:	It's raining.
Charlie:	Come away from that window, Ted.
Ted:	I'm not doing any harm.
Man's voice:	Put that light out!
	(Ted quickly closes the curtain.)
Ted:	I only opened it an inch.
Charlie:	Sit down, before you get us in more trouble.
	(Ted sits on the floor. He looks at a small clock on the table. Jean smiles at him. He scowls.)

Ted:	Is Mum going to be long?
Charlie:	She's working late.
Ted:	I'm hungry.
Charlie:	You're always hungry.
Ted:	Mum's always late. I wish she didn't work at the bomb factory.
Jean:	It was better when she had her old job at the butcher's.
Charlie:	Yeah, it was a lot safer.
Ted:	And we got free sausages.
Jean:	All you ever think about is your stomach.

Ted: I haven't had sausages for ages.

Jean: We don't get *any* decent food these days.

Charlie: *(Sighs)* It's all powdered.

Jean: Or rationed.

Ted: You can get it sometimes. I had some icing last week.

Charlie: That's impossible.

Ted: It's not. George Baxter had a load of it on his birthday cake.

Jean: That's breaking the law.

Charlie: It must have been cardboard painted to look like icing.

Ted: It wasn't. I ate some.

Charlie: I bet it tasted like cardboard.

Ted: It tasted lovely. His mum made it with *real* eggs.

Charlie: I don't believe you.

Ted: Ask George then.

Jean: You know we can't.

Charlie: He's just been evacuated.

Ted: *(Sulkily)* I wish I'd gone with him.

(Ted picks up his toy plane and divebombs the cat. It ignores him.)

Jean: (*Brightly*) Have you got this week's copy of *Aircraft Spotter*, Ted?

Ted: Yes.

Jean: Can I borrow it?

Ted: Why?

Jean: Miss North has told the class to find out lots of facts about the Junkers JU 87B. We'll probably have a test on Friday.

Charlie: The Junkers JU 87B is a German divebomber with ... let me think ... three machine guns.

Ted: And a crew of two.

Charlie: I've drawn it loads of times.

Ted: It's harder to draw than the Messerschmitt.

Charlie: But a lot easier to spell.

Jean: Can I borrow your copy, then?

Ted: I suppose so. It's on my bed.

(Jean exits stage left. Ted calls out after her.)

Ted: Don't go near my Spitfire. The glue's still setting!

Charlie: How was school today?

Ted: *(Shrugs)* Okay. This morning, I wrote two pages about what I'd do to Hitler if I caught him. I would have done more but Mr Scott said I was using up too much paper. He won't let us draw a margin any more.

Charlie: I've been writing about the things I'll do when Dad comes home at the end of the war. I think we should have a street party, with loads of flags and food.

Ted: Yeah. Fireworks lighting the sky ...

Charlie: And a banner stretched over the road saying "Welcome Home". You can eat icing until it comes out of your ears.

Ted: No, I'll be eating grapes. And bananas. George says bananas are *this* big.

(He stretches his arms out. Charlie laughs.)

Charlie: Bananas are much smaller than that.

Ted: How do you know? You haven't eaten one.

Charlie: I have. Mum bought some at the start of the war, when people could still get them. We all had one. I suppose you're too young to remember.

(Jean enters the room.)

Jean: One of the wings has dropped off your plane.

Ted: I told you not to touch it!

(He rushes past her and exits stage left.)

Jean: *(To Charlie)* It hasn't really.

(Without warning, an air raid siren begins to wail.)

Charlie: Quick, get under the table! I'll call Ted.

(Jean crawls under the table while Charlie rushes to the door. He shouts offstage to Ted.)

Charlie: It's a raid!

Ted: *(From offstage)* I bet it's a false alarm.

Charlie: Get downstairs.

(There is a pause, then Ted appears by the door.)

Ted: There was nothing wrong with my plane. *(Looks at Jean)* Another false alarm.

Charlie: It wasn't a false alarm when Mrs Jones had her house bombed with high explosives.

Jean: We found her cooker in our garden.

Charlie: That's right. And her wireless.

(Charlie crawls under the table. It is a basic Morrison shelter, lined with cushions and blankets.)

Charlie: It was a good job Mrs Jones was down at the allotments.

Jean: She was luckier than the people at number forty-seven. I hope Mum's in the factory shelter.

Charlie: She will be.

Ted: We should be in the garden.

(Ted stands by the door, stage left.)

Ted: Why don't we go to the Anderson shelter while there's still time?

Charlie: Mum says it's flooded.

Ted: It's always flooded. We can put our boots on.

Charlie: *(Weary)* Get under the table, Ted.

Ted: You two look really daft.

Charlie There's nothing daft about taking shelter. Are you coming in here or not?

Ted: I suppose so.

(He crawls under the table into the Morrison shelter.)

Jean: I heard Aunt Alice tell Mum that our Anderson shelter needs knocking down and rebuilding. The roof leaks, and water keeps seeping up through the floor.

Ted: No one thought it would have to last this long.

Charlie: *(Flat)* No one expected the *war* to last this long.

Ted: In London, people shelter in the underground stations. They sleep on the platforms. They're railway sleepers. *(He laughs.)*

Jean: It can't be very comfortable.

Charlie: At least it's safe.

Ted: I'd be really bored.

Charlie: They have talent competitions in some shelters.

Ted: *(Unimpressed)* Great.

Jean: We should have one.

Charlie: I can't sing.

Jean: You can dance.

Charlie: *(Looks around)* Not in this space.

Ted: We *could* tell jokes.

Jean: We've heard all yours.

Ted: I'll read my comic then.

(Ted picks up a Hotspur.*)*

Charlie: Have you got any more?

Ted: No. I keep this one in here for emergencies. My comics are outside in the Anderson shelter. Do you want me to go and get them?

Charlie: No. Mum's told me not to let either of you out of my sight.

Ted: I hope the rain isn't dripping on to my *Hotspurs*. I left them on my bunk.

Jean: They'll be all right.

(Ted climbs out of the shelter.)

Ted: I'll just check.

Charlie: Come back here!

Ted: *(Grins)* I'll be back in a minute.

(He runs out stage left.)

Charlie: *(Sighs)* I'll have to go after him. You know what I promised Mum.

Jean: He's only gone to the bottom of the garden. He should be ...

Charlie: Shh. Listen.

(Faint bangs can be heard in the distance.)

Charlie: It's flak. We've started sending up anti-aircraft fire. I'll have to get him.

(Charlie starts to climb out of the shelter. Jean grabs his hand.)

Jean: If you try and bring Ted back in he'll probably run off somewhere. You know what he's like.

Charlie: *(Sighs, and sits down again)* I suppose you're right. I'll give him a couple of minutes and if he's not back ... I'll go after him.

Jean: I'll come with you.

Charlie: No.

Jean: Knowing Ted, he'll sit in the shelter reading his comics.

Charlie The generator's not working. He won't have any light. Did he take his gas mask with him?

Jean: I think so.

Charlie: We should put ours on.

Jean: Mine smells rubbery.

Charlie: They all do.

(Charlie mimes the action of putting on a gas mask. Jean copies him.)

15

Jean: I wish Mum was here.

Charlie: I wish Ted was here.

Jean: He's always running off.

Charlie: Shall we put the wireless on? It'll cheer us up a bit.

Jean: I'm staying under this table until I hear the "All Clear".

Charlie: I don't know why we're both so scared. I bet the raiders are miles away. Ted's probably right. It's another false alarm.

(There is a loud explosion. The children react to this, diving for cover under the blankets.)

Jean: Charlie!

(If the table legs are shaken then objects on top of the table, including the clock, should tip over – adding to the din.)

Charlie: Keep your head down!

Jean: It *is* down.

(*Flak starts up again. This time it is deafening. Charlie and Jean lie still, listening to the constant stream of shells bursting in the sky.*)

Charlie: (*His voice shaking*) That was close. For a moment I thought we were goners.

Jean: I could feel the wind.

Charlie: That was quite a blast.

Jean: It went right through the house.

(Jean tries to take her gas mask off.)

Charlie: Leave that on!

Jean: It's all fogged up.

Charlie: There could be gas around.

Jean: Why didn't we hear any planes?

Charlie: I don't know. Maybe there was only one? A plane on its own doesn't make much noise. *(Grimly)* Until it drops a bomb.

Jean: I'm glad I wasn't outside when it went off ... that bomb was so close.

Charlie: *(Slowly)* Ted was out there.

Jean: He might have been in the garden. He could have been hit.

Charlie: It was a few streets away.

Jean: There must have been shrapnel. Do you think Ted's hurt?

Charlie: He'll be fine. (*Unsure*) He was probably in the shelter.

Jean: We'll have to look for him.

Charlie: We can't go outside. Not yet. It's too dangerous.

Jean: Will they drop another bomb?

Charlie: Who knows?

(*Jean looks around the room.*)

Jean: The clock's stopped. It's broken.

Charlie: I think it fell off the shelter.

Jean: Mum won't be very happy.

Charlie: We'll get the clock fixed.

Jean: (*Angry*) I wish this war would stop.

Charlie: It will do. One day we'll wake up and there won't be any more fighting ... and there won't be any more bombs.

Jean: Ted should have been back by now.

Charlie: If I go and scout him out, will you promise not to move?

Jean: I promise.

(*Charlie climbs out of the shelter. He puts the clock back on the table. He also picks up books that have been scattered across the room.*)

Charlie: I won't be long.

(*There is a sound of someone knocking on the door. Charlie freezes. Cautiously he walks stage left and mimes pulling on a door knob. Ted enters the mime, pushing at the door from the other side, trying to get in. Eventually the door opens and Ted falls into the room.*)

Charlie: Ted!

Ted: (*Breathless*) The door must have been blown shut by that bomb. I couldn't get back in. (*He looks round the room and whistles.*) What a mess. I told you it was safer in the other shelter.

(*Jean and Charlie take off their gas masks.*)

Jean: Is that where you've been?

Ted: Yeah, I was trying to dry out my comics. They're wet through.

Jean: I thought you were dead.

Ted: I'm all right. There's a big blaze behind the church. And I think some of the shops in the High Street are on fire. I'm glad Mum's not at the butcher's any more. I bet that's up in smoke.

Charlie: We'd better get under the table.

(They scramble into the shelter.)

Ted: It was really exciting out there.

Charlie: You nearly got yourself killed. What's that in your hand?

Ted: Nothing.

Charlie: Ted!

Ted: It's something for my collection. Just a bit of shrapnel. I heard something hit the side of the shelter, so I went outside and ... I found this. *(He holds out a piece of twisted metal.)* Have a feel.

(Charlie takes it.)

Charlie: It's still warm.

Ted: I bet there's loads more in the garden. If I had a torch I'd go and have a look.

Charlie: You're staying right here. We've had enough of your antics for one night. I ought to tell Mum about you.

Ted: I was only getting my comics. *(Sheepish)* I won't do it again.

Charlie: You'd better not.

Ted: *(Sulkily)* I've already been told off for being outside. Uncle Mick saw me as he was cycling past.

Charlie: That's too bad.

Ted: He's coming over later once they've dealt with the fire.

Jean: Does he know what caused the explosion?

Ted: Not yet. *(Pleased)* There should be lots of shrapnel lying about. I hope Uncle Mick remembers to get me some.

Jean: He'll have far more important things to think about than that.

Ted: I wish the school had been hit.

(Charlie and Jean sigh.)

Ted: No one would have been inside. *(Dreamy)* I'd like to spend the morning in school clearing away old cartridge cases, and filling in the craters.

Jean:	That sounds like hard work.
Ted:	It would be brilliant. I could really build up my bullet collection. George has got thirty cases. I need another three to catch him up.
Charlie:	I'll see if I can find you some shrapnel tomorrow.
Ted:	Great.
Jean:	Mum will go mad. She says your room already looks as if a bomb's hit it.
Ted:	What about all that scrap iron you keep in the shed? That's what I call a mess. I can't get my bike inside so it's going really rusty because of you.
Jean:	Put it on the pile then. It's all going to be recycled. Just think. Your bike could be turned into a Spitfire.
Charlie:	The world's first flying bike. You should donate it to help the war effort.
Ted:	I'll need my bike if I'm going to be an ARP warden. Anyway, I'm helping the war effort when I do school gardening, instead of games. I really hate planting carrots, and all that digging.
Charlie:	Winston Churchill says we have to dig for victory. It saves lives.
Ted:	How?

Jean: Don't you listen at school?

Charlie: If we grow our own food, then we don't have to get it from other countries.

Jean: That means our food ships won't be sunk by German submarines.

Charlie: And *that* saves sailors' lives.

Ted: Saved by a carrot.

Charlie: That's one way to look at it.

(The children look to the rear of the stage. Muffled voices can be heard outside.)

Charlie: Sshh.

Ted: German paratroopers.

Jean: Don't be silly. It sounds like Mr Maddison from next door.

Ted: I bet they're kidnapping him.

(Charlie walks to the rear of the stage and mimes lifting up the blackout curtain.)

Charlie: It's only the Home Guard. They must be going around houses checking that everything's all right.

Jean: Close the curtain, Charlie.

Ted: Yeah. We don't want to attract their attention. *(Dramatic)* They could be German Paratroopers ... disguised as the Home Guard.

(Charlie laughs.)

Ted: I'll be glad when we're evacuated.

Charlie: It won't be long now. We'll be on Aunt Sarah's farm this time next week.

Ted:	I'm going to ride a tractor.
Charlie:	You're too young.
Ted:	I'll ride a cow then.
Jean:	People don't ride cows. They milk them.
Ted:	Milk doesn't come from cows.
Charlie:	Where does it come from then?
Ted:	The dairy.
Jean:	He's in for a shock. We'll have to help with the harvest.
Charlie:	Throwing hay bales on to carts.
Jean:	Picking hops.
Charlie:	And potatoes. Should be great fun.
Ted:	I hope they sell comics in the country.
Jean:	You'll be too tired to read them.

Ted: Will there be a school?

Jean: Yes. Even in the country.

Charlie: I can't wait to go.

(The flak eases off a little.)

Charlie: I can't wait for *this* to stop.

(They stop talking and listen to occasional bursts of flak.)

Charlie: I'll be sorry to leave this place.

Jean: We'll come back when the fighting is over.

Ted: If the house is still standing.

Charlie: It will be. They wouldn't dare have a direct hit on your comic collection.

Ted: Mum says I can take it with me.

Charlie: In that case, *you* can carry it.

Jean: Will this war ever be over?

Charlie: By Christmas. That's what the newspapers say.

Jean: They say that every year.

Charlie: One day they'll be right.

Ted: When it's over will I get a new pair of shoes?

Jean: You'll have anything you want.

Ted: Will I have my dad back?

Charlie: I hope so. I really do hope so.

(The flak starts up again, and this time it is much closer. There is a chill in the air, and the children huddle under the blankets.)

Charlie: There are some things I can't promise.

Ted   *(Softly)* He'll be back. I know he will.

(The three children sit in silence, listening to the noise around them. There is a knock at the door. They look at each other.)

Choosing Parts

The parts of Ted, Charlie and Jean should be read by confident readers. The character of the Man has only one line and he is not seen.

Putting On the Play

You may wish to put on a performance of the play, rather than just reading it. The following suggestions may provide you with a starting point for your own ideas about staging a production. Obviously, the use you make of these suggestions will vary depending on the time and resources available to your school.

For permission to put on a profit-making performance of *Taking Shelter*, please contact the Editorial Department, Ginn & Co. Ltd, Prebendal House, Parson's Fee, Aylesbury, Bucks HP20 2QZ. (There is no need to apply for permission if you are not charging an entrance fee, but please let us know if you are putting on any performance of this play, as we would be interested to hear about it.)

Staging

The action takes place in the children's front room. How realistic this is in terms of period setting obviously depends on the resources available. Minimal staging is needed for a basic production – a table big enough for three children to sit under, a chair and a few blankets and pillows will suffice. If more resources are available, a period sitting-room could be constructed using flats, scenery and a replica Morrison Shelter. See the illustrations in the main body of the book for more ideas.

Costumes

Charlie wears a school uniform – perhaps black shorts, a white shirt, a grey jumper, grey socks, black shoes and a school tie.
Ted could wear a pair of grey shorts, a white shirt and a knitted pullover.
Jean could wear a plain blue dress, white socks and a pair of slippers.
Gas masks could prove difficult to make, and in any case they may make the children's speech inaudible. The script suggests miming putting on the gas masks. However, if you want to use real gas masks, these can be obtained from Army Surplus stores.

Props

Blankets and pillows to go under the table.
A newspaper, some crayons and a small clock to go on top of the table.
A toy plane for **Ted** to play with.
A toy cat (optional).
Books for **Charlie** to read. These will be scattered across the floor during the explosion.
Two comics – one to go under the table, one to be brought in by **Jean**.
A piece of shrapnel, perhaps made of silver foil, for **Ted** to bring in.

Sound Effects

The sounds of flak and a large explosion are called for. These will be available on sound-effect records or tapes from the local library or record shop. The explosion could also be represented using a synthesiser.

Follow-up Work

Research

Encourage the children to research the background of the play. They could investigate the following:

- Civilian life in World War 2;
- Rationing;
- Children's leisure activities;
- Evacuation;
- Propaganda;
- The blitz;
- Women working in factories;
- The effects of the war on schools;
- Air raid procedures – ARP wardens, blackouts, sirens etc.

Drama

Rehearsed Improvisation

The play ends with a knock on the door. Split the class into groups of four to five, and ask the groups to produce a rehearsed improvisation about what happens after the knock. The pupils should think about who is at the door, and what news that person is bringing.

Hot-seating

Hot-seating is a strategy which can help pupils either to create a character or to develop greater understanding of a character in the text.

1. Put a chair at the front of the class and arange the rest of the class in a semicircle around it.

2. Choose a child to represent one of the characters in the play, and ask him or her to sit in the hot seat.

3. The rest of the class must ask the child questions, which he or she has to answer in role – in other words, as the character.

The object is to explore the characters' motivation for acting as they do.

One by one, put the characters of Ted,

Charlie and Jean in the hot seat. Some questions to ask Charlie:

- Do you like looking after your brother and sister?
- Do they ever annoy you?
- Why don't you ever admit to Ted and Jean that you are frightened?

To Ted:

- Why don't you do as your brother tells you?
- Why don't you tell Charlie or Jean that you get worried when your mum is at the factory?

To Jean:

- What do you thmk about Ted and Charlie?
- Do they annoy you?
- Do you get frightened during air raids?

Creating Characters

Follow the above guidelines for hot-seating, but this time the person in the hot seat should make up information about a new character, who doesn't actually appear in the play. The best one to start with may be the children's mother. Begin with easy questions ("What is your name? How old are you?") before moving on to more difficult ones ("How do you feel when you are at the factory and the children are at home?")

Other characters to create in this way could be the children's father, a teacher at their school, their Aunt Alice, and George Baxter. These characters can then be used in an improvisation to extend the play, or in an entirely different scene.